# CONTENTS

# A YEAR OF FUN

Exciting changes are always happening on Club Penguin, and this past year was no different. Penguins got to play new games, explore newly designed rooms, and even adopt a brand new puffle! Which was your favourite highlight from 2011?

> I love the brown puffle's inventive spirit.

## PUFFLE-PALOOZA

2011 was a great year for puffles. The Pet Shop got a fun new look—and a new game, Puffle Launch. Adopting and caring for puffles is still as exciting as ever before, and for the first time, penguins could give their puffle a fabulous hairstyle. We even discovered the brown puffle during the Wilderness Expedition in January!

> Playing games in the Dance Lounge is a great way to chill after a dance party.

## GAME TIME

Club Penguin welcomed spring with a fresh new look for the game arcade in the Dance Lounge.

## NEW STAMPS

Dozens of new Stamps were released, and penguins scrambled to add them to their Stamp Books.

> If you meet me you'll earn a fine lookin' Stamp!

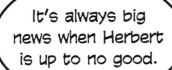

> It's always big news when Herbert is up to no good.

## FIELD-OPS

Herbert P. Bear and his sidekick, Klutzy the Crab continued to try to sabotage the island. EPF agents worked together to complete Field-Ops and stop his evil plans.

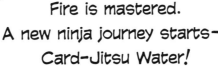

> Fire is mastered. A new ninja journey starts— Card-Jitsu Water!

## THE ELEMENT OF WATER

After working hard to master Card-Jitsu Fire, ninjas got the chance to test their skills against the second element: Water.

# TALKIN' WITH ROCKHOPPER

Captain Rockhopper is usually out sailing the seven seas with his puffle, Yarr, but we caught up to him the last time he docked the Migrator at Club Penguin. After he sang us some sea shanties and told us about his latest pirate adventure, he answered a few questions for us.

Q: You have found many treasures in your travels. Which is your most prized possession?
Rockhopper: Arrr! The Migrator. I built it with me own two flippers!

Q: You must need to bring a lot of provisions with you when you go on a long voyage. What's the one thing you're always sure to bring?
Rockhopper: I like to keep me stocks of cream soda high, matey!

Q: Every year, penguins look forward to the games and prizes you bring for The Fair. What's your favourite game to play?
Rockhopper: All the games be fun. But by far me favorite isn't at a booth. It's our own games of hide 'n seek with Yarr and all me good penguin friends.

Q: Whenever you're on the island, penguins are anxious to meet you in person. What's the best way for them to find you?
Rockhopper: I like to be movin' around. Just look for me — the red penguin lookin' for stinky cheese, makin' a bit o' noise and tellin' adventure stories.

Thanks, Captain Rockhopper!
Rockhopper: Yer mighty welcome!

# SEA MAIL

You've got a new message—and it's a postcard from Captain Rockhopper! Read the postcard and then write one back to Captain Rockhopper, telling him what you've been doing on Club Penguin.

Ahoy matey!

You won't believe what me and Yarr ran into while sailin' the seas—a mighty monster of a whale! At first, we feared the great beast might harm the Migrator. Luckily, she was fond o' cream soda!

-ROCKHOPPER

# WORD TREASURE HUNT

Captain Rockhopper searches for treasure on remote islands. Search the words Rockhopper, Migrator and Treasure to see how many smaller words you can make from the letters of each one. Write your answers on the lines below each word.

## ROCKHOPPER
**Example: hope**

## MIGRATOR
**Example: goat**

## TREASURE
**Example: tea**

# SHIVER ME TIMBERS!

On a long sea voyage, Captain Rockhopper loves to pass the time by telling jokes to Yarr, his red puffle. Here are some of his favourite pirate jokes.

**What grades did the pirate get on his report card?**
High C's!

**What's on the bottom of the sea and shivers?**
A nervous wreck!

**What do you call a happy flag?**
A Jolly Roger!

**Why are fish so smart?**
Because they're always in schools!

**Why did the pirate become a basketball star?**
Because he had a great hook shot!

**What part of a fish weighs the most?**
The scales!

**How did the pirate buy the ship so cheaply?**
Because it was on sail!

**What movie did the pirate go to?**
The one that was rated Aarrrrrrr!

# MIGRATOR MAZE

Rockhopper and Yarr are trying to bring a new load of treasures to Club Penguin. Can you get them to the island safely?

START

# TELESCOPE TEST

Look through these telescope lenses and you'll spy two pictures of Rockhopper and Yarr. The pictures look similar, but the second picture is different than the first in eight ways. Can you spot and circle all the differences?

# ASK AUNT ARCTIC

Not only is Aunt Arctic editor-in-chief of The Club Penguin Times, she also gives advice to readers in her column "Ask Aunt Arctic." She's got the inside scoop on everything from the latest Club Penguin party to island secrets. We wanted to learn more about the penguin with all the answers, so we sat down in Aunt Arctic's igloo to ask her questions—this time, about herself!

Q: Cool igloo! You've got a lot of interesting items in here. Do you enjoy collecting things?
Aunt Arctic: Indeed! Each of the things in my igloo tells a story and reminds me of something interesting that has happened.

Q: What do you like best about your igloo?
Aunt Arctic: There is no one best thing. My igloo is the place where I can relax after a long day of investigative reporting!

Q: Who is your best friend?
Aunt Arctic: Best friends, you mean! My puffles, of course.

Q: There's always something fun to do on Club Penguin. What's your favourite way to spend time?
Aunt Arctic: I love finding newsworthy stories to write about.

Thank you, Aunt Arctic.
Aunt Arctic: You're welcome! I always enjoy answering questions.

# A MEETING MIX-UP

Aunt Arctic has scheduled interviews with four penguins for The Club Penguin Times. She wrote down where she needs to meet each one, but a hungry orange puffle ate her notes by mistake! Can you help Aunt Arctic figure out where to meet each penguin? Use the clues to help you.

1 The pink penguin will be at a place where penguins can use coins to buy things.

2 The black penguin is meeting Aunt Arctic at a place that you can't walk to.

3 There is no mini-game at the spot where the purple penguin is waiting for Aunt Arctic.

4 The lime green penguin is waiting somewhere in the Plaza.

| | PET SHOP | ICEBERG | GIFT SHOP | STADIUM |
| --- | --- | --- | --- | --- |
| BLACK PENGUIN | | | | |
| PINK PENGUIN | | | | |
| LIME GREEN PENGUIN | | | | |
| PURPLE PENGUIN | | | | |

# FIND YOUR INNER PENGUIN POET

Roses are red
Violets are blue
Aunt Arctic is a writer
And you could be too!

Discover the penguin poet inside of you! Writing poems is a fun way to express how you feel about your favourite things in Club Penguin. Get started by learning about two different types of poems – haiku and limericks – and then try writing some of your own.

## Haiku

Haiku is a form of Japanese poetry. (It also happens to be Sensei's favourite kind!) The first and last lines of a haiku have five syllables; the middle line has seven. A syllable is the number of sounds, or beats, in each word. For example, penguin has two syllables: pen-guin. Here are some examples of haikus:

Jet Pack Adventure
Soaring through the skies
Collecting coins as we go
Watch out for anvils!

Brown Puffle
My super smart pet
Helps me with science homework
Can your dog do that?

Ready to give it a try?
Write your own haiku on the lines below:

# Limericks

Limericks are five-line poems. In limericks, the first, second and fifth lines of the poem rhyme with each other, while the last word in lines three and four should rhyme, too. Here are some examples:

Cadence
Cadence grooves to her own special beat.
Some would say she's got magical feet.
She's the talk of the town.
When she dances around.
She's the penguin we all want to meet!

Drilling Party
Some penguins are hoping to see,
The big Iceberg tip into the sea.
They dance and they jump,
They drill and they bump.
But that Iceberg's as firm as can be.

Now it's your turn to write a limerick. Have fun!

# FIND THE MISSING COLUMNS

Stop the presses! Penguins are eagerly waiting for the newest issue of The Club Penguin Times. But there was a mix-up and all of this week's columns have gone missing!

Help Aunt Arctic by finding and circling the names of the lost columns in this word search puzzle. Remember to search backwards, forwards, and diagonally.

```
G T Z F E N O Z K C U B A G U Y
B J Y G L Z B Q K I P N Z E F D
N C O I F T Q U O T C E G T Y N
L S Z H Y D F Y F C O X N P G E
T R U C R Q J F F R M T G U V W
T J H Q O H O D J A I H I B G S
I S R C T R K Y W T N I E L A F
S Z T E S P E S T N G D L I R L
E T S E E B S A W U E D I S V A
E I B H R U E B V A V E E H P S
V L D L U C L F X K E N O E J H
H M R O T W E V M S N P I D U G
J Y G S A Z F S F A T I P L E P
M U E V E B H O W B S N G L G A
H Q N F F R G U S R I D D L E S
K C D X Z C C F C K T W Z V A N
```

## WORD BANK:

ASK AUNT ARCTIC — JOKES — RIDDLES
FEATURE STORY — NEWS FLASH — SECRETS
GET PUBLISHED — NEXT HIDDEN PIN — UPCOMING EVENTS

# PUFFLE PROBLEM

Aunt Arctic brought her beloved pet puffles into the office with her. To help her out, the puffles decided to type up some newspaper headlines. But they don't know how to type! See if you can unscramble the words below to find the real headlines:

1  Wen Ufpfle Discoedrev _____

2  Porchpoker Reviewtin _____

3  Elffup Patry Si Ehre _____

4  Ratwe Ojod Rout Whit Seesin _____

5  Ninepug Cometus Scentto _____

6  Ear Eelti Gasten Magno Su? _____

7  Ni Elyst Thiw Cancede _____

8  Gray's Tagged Viewer _____

9  Pits Fro Miin-Asgem _____

10  Yemstry Hips Dotspet Ta Cabhe _____

## HEADLINES:

Are Elite Agents Among Us?
Gary's Gadget Review
In Style with Cadence
Mystery Ship Spotted at Beach
New Puffle Discovered

Penguin Costume Contest
Puffle Party is Here
Rockhopper Interview
Tips for Mini-Games
Water Dojo Tour with Sensei

# A MYSTERIOUS MISSION

"Go Blue Team! You can do it!"

You're hanging out in Penguin Stadium with your friend, watching a soccer game between the Red Team and the Blue Team. Right now, the score is tied, but a Blue Team player has the ball and is heading toward the Red Team's goal. A red player slides up behind her, but she scoots ahead, and then she shoots . . .

"Goal!" you cry happily. "Go Blue!"

Suddenly, you feel a buzzing in your pocket. It's your Elite Penguin Force Spy Phone. You friend is distracted by the game, so you turn to the side and touch the flashing screen.

It's a message from G. He's got a new Field-Ops for you—a special mission you need to complete. You're excited. You have more than twenty Field-Op Medals. It's time to add one more.

"Gotta run," you tell your friend.

Your friend looks puzzled. "But the game's just getting exciting."

Although you wish you could tell your friend about the Field-Op, it's important to keep your identity as an Elite Agent a secret.

"I forgot to feed my puffle," you say, and your friend nods. "I'll catch up with you later."

You quickly waddle out of the stadium and when you're sure you're alone, you press a button on your Spy Phone and instantly transport to EPF Command. The place is bustling with other agents eager to complete the latest Field-Op. Some of them are gathered around the big conference table, discussing their strategy. You head to the big computer screen that reads "Field-Ops" and check in.

A picture of G appears on the screen, with these instructions:

"Agent, Herbert P. Bear is up to more suspicious activity. To thwart his latest efforts, I need you to locate three items: a battery, a heating coil, and a magnifying glass. When you have gathered all three, bring them to the tallest tree in the Forest and await further instructions."

The screen goes blank, and you step back. It's a curious assignment. You don't remember G asking you to gather items before.

But if that's what G needs, you'll do

it. You're an EPF agent, after all. It's your job to get a battery, a heating coil, and a magnifying glass. Now which item should you find first?

You might as well go in order. A battery shouldn't be too hard to find, should it? You think of all of the places where you might find something battery operated. Then you activate your Spy Phone and teleport directly to the Night Club.

Inside, the dance floor is crowded with dancing penguins. You notice that most of them are dressed in their best clothes and wigs. Everyone looks pretty fab. You're tempted to join in the dance, but then you remember you're on a mission.

You waddle up to the DJ3K booth, where a penguin in headphones is spinning the turntables and tapping his feet to the beat. You look around, hoping to find an extra pair of headphones that might hold a battery you can use.

"Screeeech!" The high-pitched sound fills the Night Club, and suddenly the music stops. The DJ looks down at his flipper and frowns—the arm of the turntable has popped right off!

The dancers moan with disappointment. You know you're on a mission, but you suspect you can do something to help. You're an EPF agent, after all, and you've pledged to help all of the penguins on the island.

"What seems to be the matter?" you ask.

"I'm not sure," the DJ admits. "The thing just snapped off."

You take a closer look. There is a small metal pin that connects the arm to the base of the turntable, and the DJ is right—it's snapped in half. But it should be an easy fix.

"We just need a replacement for the pin," you say thoughtfully, gazing around the Night Club. There must be something you can use.

Then you see something sparkle in the reflection of the coloured spotlights—copper earrings, dangling from the Boho wig of a pink penguin.

"Excuse me, but may I have one of your earrings?" you ask the penguin. "I need to fix the turntable."

She smiles. "Sure, if it'll get the music back on."

She hands you the earring and you take off the pin, straighten it with a handy tool from your Spy Phone, and use it to reattach the arm of the turntable. The DJ tests it out–and it's perfect!

"Thanks!" he calls out over the music.

"No problem," you say. "But I was wondering–do you have an extra battery I could have?"

"You got it," the DJ replies. "I always carry extras for my MP 3000 player."

He hands you a battery, and you thank him and slip it into your backpack. Then you exit the Night Club, waving to the happy dancers as you go.

You check your Spy Phone for the next item on the list: a heating coil. Right next door is the Coffee Shop. You've worked there before, and you seem to remember seeing a heating coil in one of the coffee makers. Perfect!

Inside the Coffee Shop, a few penguins are sitting at tables, drinking cups of cocoa or reading the newspaper. A barista in a green apron is standing behind the service counter. The orange penguin looks puzzled, and you notice she's staring at several scraps of paper.

"Hi there," you say. "Is everything okay?"

"Oh, it's fine, I guess," she replies. "It's just that when I came to work I found a piece of paper on the floor. I thought it was trash so I tore it up. But as I was about to throw it out I realized that there's writing on the other side. It's my manager's handwriting. She must have left me a message, but I can't read it now."

"Let me take a look," you say.

The barista steps aside and you see that she has torn the paper into eight pieces. Each piece has a word on it:

"bowls please The them. empty, are sugar fill"

It looks like a message. You stare at the words for a bit. The message must begin with "The" and end with "them." But what's in between?

You rearrange the scraps of paper and then cry out triumphantly.

"I've got it!"

The barista looks over your shoulder and reads aloud. "The sugar bowls are empty, please fill them."

She nods. "Of course. That makes sense. I wish there was some way I could thank you."

"Actually, there is," you say. "I'm looking for a heating coil, like the one you use in the coffee machines."

The barista frowns. "I wish I could help you, but we need them to run the machines," she says. Then she gets a bright look on her face. "Wait! There's an old machine underneath the counter. You could have the one from that."

She rummages under the counter and gives you the heating coil.

"Thanks," you say, slipping it into your backpack.

"What do you need a heating coil for, anyway?" she asks.

"That information is classified," you reply, in your best EPF voice. Then you quickly leave before she can ask any more questions.

The last item G requested is a magnifying glass. You're a bit stumped about where you will find one. Then

two penguins walk past you, and you overhear their lively discussion.

"'Fairy Fables' was my favourite play ever," one penguin is saying.

"That was good, but 'The Penguins That Time Forgot' is more action packed," says the other.

Hearing them reminds you of one of your favourite plays–"Ruby and the Ruby", about a detective searching for a missing gem. Detectives use magnifying glasses to look for clues. Maybe you can find one in an old costume trunk.

It's a short walk to the Plaza, so you waddle to the Stage as quickly as you can. The name of the play on the marquee is that sci-fi favourite, "Squidzoid vs. Shadow Guy and Gamma Gal". Inside, the set onstage looks like a cityscape. A giant monster is popping out of one of the rooftops. A yellow penguin in a director's cap is pacing back and forth across the stage. He looks upset.

"Is everything all right?" you ask.

"No, it's the exact opposite of all right!" the director wails. "This play is supposed to go on in an hour and my leading lady had to quit because her football team has a big game. What am I going to do? We can't have a play without Gamma Gal!"

"What kind of actor do you need to play Gamma Gal?" you ask.

"Gamma Gal is brave! She's bold! She's daring!" the director says.

"So I need to find a superhero?" you ask.

The director shrugs. "Actually, I just need someone with a good attitude who wants to be in a play."

You think you know just the penguin. "I think I can help," you tell him. "I'll be right back."

You transport to the Night Club, and are relieved to see the pink penguin in the Boho wig who gave you her earring. She's still dancing away.

"How would you like to star in a play?" you ask her.

She smiles. "Really? That sounds like fun!" she replies.

"Great! Follow me," you say.

You guessed that the pink penguin had just the right attitude to play Gamma Gal, and you were right. When the two of you enter the theater, the director is overjoyed.

"She's perfect for the part!" he swoons.

"Because she looks like Gamma Gal?" you ask.

"Yes," he replies. "And because she's here! Thank you so much. If you ever need my help in return, just ask."

"Do you mind if I look through your old costume trunks?" you ask. "I need to find a magnifying glass."

"Check the "Ruby and the Ruby" trunk," he tells you.

You head backstage and find old props and costumes from all of the plays at The Stage. The trunk marked "Ruby and the Ruby" has exactly what you need—a magnifying glass.

"Fantastic!" you cry. You're about to complete your mission!

You check your Spy Phone—G wants you to bring the items to the tallest tree in the Forest. You quickly head down the snowy path and reach your destination. As you look around, trying to find the tallest tree, you notice some strange tracks on the ground. They're definitely not penguin tracks. They're too big to be penguin tracks, and they're the wrong shape—they're more round.

"Hmmm," you say thoughtfully. "Something's not right here."

You have a hunch. To be safe, you quickly teleport to your Igloo and take care of something. Then you teleport right back to the Forest.

Soon you find the tallest tree, which towers above the rest. You slowly walk up to it and then say in a loud voice.

"All right, I have the battery, the heating coil and the magnifying glass," you announce. "What do I do next?"

"You give them to me!"

You turn at the sound of the gruff voice. It's Herbert P. Bear! The furry fiend grabs your backpack and laughs triumphantly.

"That was easier than taking candy from a baby!" he growls. "I knew outsmarting you smarty pants agents would be easy."

"How did you do it?" you ask.

"I hacked into the EPF communications system," he bragged. "I need a battery, a heating coil, and a magnifying glass for my latest diabolical device. But there's no way I could get into the Coffee Shop, the Night Club or the Stage without being noticed. So I needed one of you to do it for me."

You grin. "That's exactly what I suspected!" you reveal. "I thought this mission was suspicious right from the beginning. Then when I saw those big tracks in the snow, I knew you were behind it somehow. That's why I made sure you wouldn't get your paws on the items."

Herbert looks puzzled. "But I have your backpack!"

He tears it open with his claws and dumps out the contents. Pajamas and a pair of bunny slippers tumble out into the snow.

"I transported to my Igloo and switched my backpack with my overnight bag," you tell him. "Pretty clever, huh?"

Herbert scoops up the clothes and slippers. "Oh yeah? Well . . . well . . . these pajamas are mine now. Ha!"

He starts to run away, and you realize that you have the rare opportunity to capture Herbert once and for all. You chase after him as he crashes through the trees.

Herbert leads you to the top of a tall hill. It's hard to scramble up,

because the slides are slick with ice. But Herbert's sharp claws allow him to easily get to the top first. Then, to your surprise, you see him put on the bunny slippers.

"Say hi to the rest of your Extremely Puny Friends for me!" he calls out. Then he slides down the slick hill in the bunny slippers. They're smooth on the bottom, and he slides down at rocket speed.

You keep chasing, but it's no use. He disappears into the snowy hills in the distance. Exhausted, you sit down on a rock and try to catch your breath

Your Spy Phone rings. It's G!

"Agent, are you all right?" he asks. "Our satellites have detected Herbert in the vicinity. He hacked into the EPF communications system. Did he get the items he needed for his diabolical device?"

"Negative, G," you reply. "I switched the items with some bunny slippers. But I couldn't catch him. He got away."

"Good work, agent," G replies. "You did your best. And it was very clever of you to switch the items. I'm glad we have agents like you working for the EPF."

You're sorry you didn't catch Herbert, but G's words make you very proud.

"Thanks, G!" you say. "Now is there a real Field-Ops I can do? I really want to earn another Medal!"

The End

SKI LIFT 1000

TOASTER 1000

KABOOM

ORANGE JUICE 1000

# GREETING GARY

Speaking with Gary the Gadget Guy, Club Penguin's resident inventor, was no easy thing to do! We had to go through many security clearances to get inside the Elite Penguin Force (EPF) Command Room.  Gary, also known as G, works at the EPF. He makes all the equipment EPF agents use to keep Club Penguin safe.

Q: A lot has changed since the Penguin Secret Agency headquarters was destroyed by the popcorn explosion. What do you think of the EPF and the new Command Room?
Gary: I can't say too much about the Command Room. But as you can see, a multitude of agents are here working to protect the island.

Q: What inventions are you working on now?
Gary: I'm afraid that information is classified.

Q: Rumour has it that you invented the Pizzatron 3000 because pizza is your favourite food. Is this true?
Gary: Fish Dish Pizza. Delectable. Incredible. Meritorious. That means I love it.

Q: You work a lot! Do you ever have time to play any of the games on the island?
Gary: You may find this hard to believe, but playing games often helps my brain solve problems I've been thinking about.

Thanks, Gary.
Gary: I hope my answers were helpful to you.

# BE INVENTIVE!

Gary is always coming up with new ideas. He is the inventor behind Club Penguin favourites such as the Pizzatron 3000, the Jet Pack, the snowball-powered clock and much more.

Use your imagination to create a new invention for Club Penguin. Here are some things to think about to get you started:

- What is your favourite game? What could you invent to help you perform better in the game?
- There are a few ways to get around Club Penguin. Can you think of a faster or more fun way?
- Do you have any puffles? Maybe you can invent something to help you play with them or take care of them.

**TITLE OF YOUR INVENTION:**

_____

**WHAT DOES YOUR INVENTION DO?**

_____

**DRAW YOUR INVENTION HERE:**

# MAKE YOUR OWN PIZZA

Thanks to Gary, the Pizzatron 3000 helps workers at the Pizza Parlor make lots of delicious pizzas quickly. But you don't need Gary's invention to make your own delicious pizza. Just follow this easy recipe (and make sure you get an adult to help you).

**Prep Time:** 50 min.
**Cook Time:** 14 min.
**Ready in:** 1 hour and 4 min.
**Yield:** 2-4 servings

## Directions

1. Put the flour into a large bowl, then stir in the yeast, salt and sugar.
2. Pour warm water and the olive oil into the bowl.
3. Mix everything together until the dough is soft and fairly wet.
4. Turn the dough onto a lightly-floured surface and knead for 5 minutes until smooth.
5. Cover with a tea towel and set aside for 30 minutes.
6. Meanwhile, pre-heat oven to approx. 230C/Gas mark 8.
7. Roll out the dough until it is a similar size to the tray.
8. Put the dough on the tray and add the sauce and cheese.
9. Add your favourite toppings.
10. Bake at 230C/Gas mark 8 for 14 minutes or until golden brown.

## YOU WILL NEED:

A large bowl
Tea towel
Rolling pin
Baking tray
1 cup warm water
1 1/2 tsp. of active dry yeast
2 cups bread flour
1 tbsp. olive oil
1 tsp. salt
1/2 tsp. sugar
1 can tomato sauce
Mozzarella cheese, shredded
Toppings

# GARY'S MEMORY TEST

Sometimes a good memory is the only gadget you need! Study this picture carefully. Then turn the page and see how many questions you can answer correctly without peeking.

# MEMORY TEST: YOUR ANSWERS

1   How many puffles are there?

_____

2   How many penguins are pictured?

_____

3   What does the red penguin have on his head?

_____

4   What colour are the puffles seen in the picture?

_____

5   What are the penguins doing?

_____

6   What is the penguin in the red hoodie holding?

_____

7   What is there a picture of on the red penguin's shirt?

_____

8   Which colour puffle is leaping into the air?

_____

9   What is growing on the bush?

_____

10   Which colour puffle has its eyes closed?

_____

# EPF CROSSWORD PUZZLE

The penguin agents in the Elite Penguin Force are great at finding clues to solve problems. Can you use these clues to fill in the answer in this crossword puzzle?

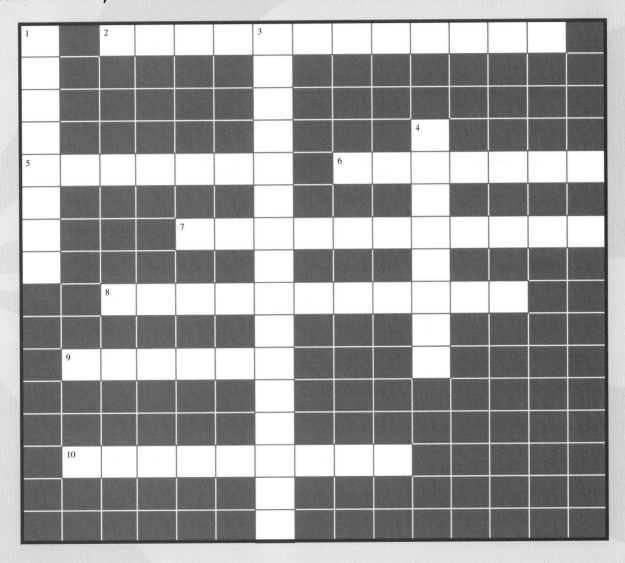

## ACROSS

2. This is another name for the VR Room, which you can only access by Tube Transport

5. This power-hungry polar bear destroyed the original Secret Agents Headquarters

6. An EPF agents' weekly assignment is called this

7. Mysterious penguin who leads the Elite Penguin Force

8. This is where EPF agents go to get their latest assignment

9. Gary the Gadget Guy's EPF name

10. Special clothes that EPF agents wear

## DOWN

1. An EPF never leaves home without this

3. This penguin creates all of the equipment EPF agents use.

4. Agents can do this to get to another part of Club Penguin Island

# BEAN COUNTERS BOARD GAME

The Coffee Shop is out of coffee! They need more coffee beans, and you can help! Be the first player to unload all the bags of beans from the delivery truck to win.

**For 2- 4 players**
**What You'll Need:**
• One six-sided dice
• Game pieces: you can use a different coloured jellybean for each player, or a different coin

**How to Play:**
Choose a game piece. Let the youngest player roll first, and then follow the directions on the square. First player to land on or past the finish line wins!

6

**7**
Get hit by an anvil. Move back 1 space.

**8**

**9**
Carry 4 bags. Move forward 4 spaces.

**10**
Get hit by a fish. Move back 2 spaces.

**13**

**12**
Carry 5 bags. Move forward 5 spaces.

**11**
Carry 4 bags. Move forward 4 spaces.

**23**
Carry 1 bag. Move forward 1 space.

**24**

**25**
Get hit by an anvil. Move back 1 space.

**FINISH**

# SENSEI SAYS

We stopped by the Dojo to speak with Sensei, a wise penguin who instructs penguins on the way of the ninja. Everyone knows that Sensei is a Card-Jitsu master, but what about the penguin behind the legend? Here's what we found out:

Q: You spend most of your time at the Dojo. What other places on the island do you like to visit?
Sensei: Club Penguin Island—
A place of much mystery
I like to explore.

Q: Do you like puffles? If so, what is your favourite kind?
Sensei: Puffles? Very cute.
The two who guard the Dojo—
They're my favourite.

Q: When it's snack time, what do you reach for
Sensei: My favourite snacks
Are things that make me stronger.
And...lots of hot sauce.

Q: After a busy day training penguins, how do you relax?
Sensei: Watching penguins play...
Increasing skills and power...
That is relaxing.

Thank you, Sensei.
Sensei: You are very welcome.

# PUFFLE PATTERNS

As Sensei knows, all ninjas must be very observant. Nothing can escape their trained eyes. Put your observation and logic skills to the test with this puffle puzzle. Each line shows a different puffle pattern. Can you figure out the missing puffle? Draw the puffle in the last box to complete the pattern.

1  

2  

3  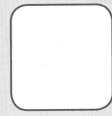

4  

5  

# SENSEI'S SEARCH

If you have a Sensei card in your Card-Jitsu deck, you are very lucky indeed. The card has the chilling power of 12 Snow. But a frosty wind whipped up and blew away Sensei's card. Can you help lead Sensei around the water, fire, and snow obstacles to find it?

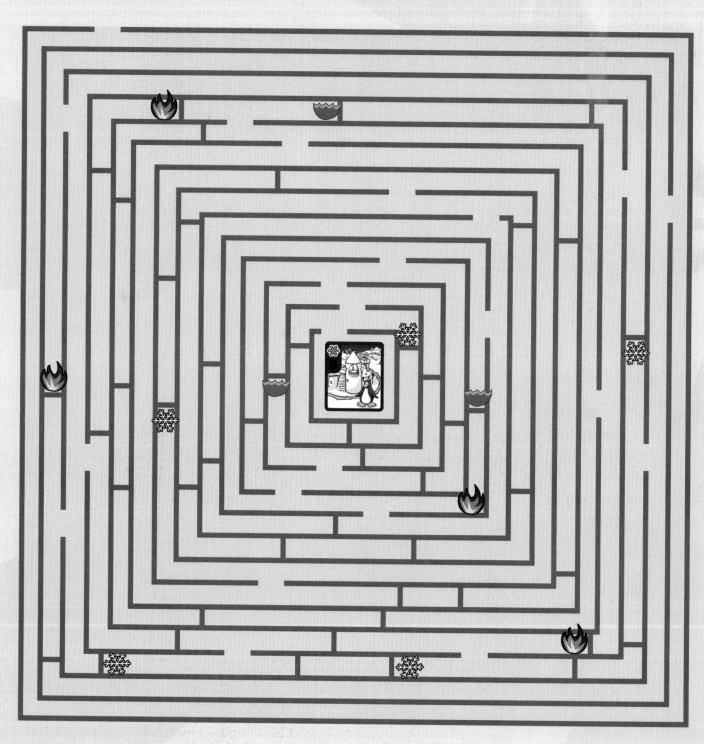

# SPOT THE DIFFERENCES

Here is another chance to test your powers of observation. You may have played Card-Jitsu Fire before, but have you ever noticed your surroundings? Look at these two pictures of the Fire Dojo. Ten things have been changed on the picture on the bottom. See if you can spot and circle the differences.

# A SURPRISE FOR SENSEI

It was a typical afternoon at the Ninja Hideout. Penguins of all different colours waddled around inside. Some wore ninja outfits. Others wore t-shirts, or dresses, or boots—clothes you would see anywhere in Club Penguin. But they all had one thing in common. They had mastered the art of Card-Jitsu, earned a black belt and challenged Sensei to become ninjas.

One ninja excitedly walked up to the Flying Flippers Emporium, a shop inside the Hideout that sells special ninja items.

"I've been saving my coins to buy a Dojo igloo and I finally have enough," she said to the penguin next to her. "I can't wait to start decorating!"

While some ninjas shopped, others were busy keeping their Card-Jitsu skills in shape by training with each other on the practice mats. Hot sauce sizzled and snowballs and water balloons flew through the air as the ninjas showed off

their mastery of snow, fire and water.

While the ninjas played Card-Jitsu, shopped, and chatted together, a yellow penguin moved to the centre of the room. He was wearing an all-black ninja outfit, belt and mask.

"Can I have everyone's attention please?" he called over the noise of the busy Hideout. The room got quiet as the ninjas turned to look at him. "I'd like to call a ninja meeting. It's important," he said.

The ninjas stopped what they were doing to gather round the yellow penguin, a ninja named Dan.

"Thank you," Dan said. "I have been doing some thinking lately about Sensei. He has done so much for us. Not only has he taught us the secrets of fire, water and snow, but he has spent hours training each and every one of us. He is always there to encourage us when we get discouraged. And he has never asked for anything in return."

The ninjas nodded in agreement.

"Like the Iceberg, Sensei is cool!" one ninja called out, and everyone cheered.

Dan smiled. "But how do we repay Sensei for everything he has done for us? I think we need to come up with a way to thank Sensei."

"Great idea!" a pink penguin called out.

"How about a parade in his honour?" one ninja suggested.

"Or a party?" another chimed in.

"We could make a statue of Sensei," added a penguin wearing a ninja Fire Suit.

"Those are all good ideas," Dan answered. "But Sensei is a pretty chill penguin. How about something more low-key?"

Kit, the penguin who was shopping for a new Dojo igloo, waved her flipper in the air. "Why don't we get him a present?"

The ninjas all liked that idea. Everyone began talking about the perfect gift for Sensei.

"We could get him a television set!" one ninja suggested.

"Or a popcorn maker!"

"How about a rock climbing wall?"

Dan spoke up. "Sensei likes to live simply. I'm not sure if he needs any of those things."

The Dojo got quiet as all the ninjas tried to think of the perfect present. Then Kit spoke up again.

"Why don't we cook Sensei a special dinner as a surprise? Every penguin has got to eat!" she said.

Everyone began murmuring in agreement. Yes, a special dinner for Sensei was the perfect present!

"But what will we make?" someone asked.

Dan clapped his flippers. "Aha! I got it! We can make a meal that represents each of the elements: fire, water and snow. Let's split up into three teams. Each team will make a dish inspired by their element."

"I'll be the leader of the Fire team," offered the penguin in the Fire Suit. "My name's Red."

"I'll lead the Water team," Kit spoke up.

"Great!" said Dan. "And I'll lead the Snow team."

The ninjas quickly gathered into three groups.

"We will all meet at the Dojo when we have finished cooking our dishes for Sensei," Dan said. "He'll be so surprised!"

The teams began to talk about what they should make.

"Fire Team—what dish should we cook?" Red asked his teammates.

"Something spicy, of course! Hot sauce is the way to go!" a penguin called out.

"Perfect!" Red cried. "How about a spicy pizza? I know that's my favourite when I go to the Pizza Parlor."

The Fire Team ninjas liked that idea. "Let's go to The Plaza!" one yelled.

The ninjas made their way from the Hideout to the Plaza. As soon as they walked into the Pizza Parlor, they could tell something was wrong.

No smell of delicious pizza baking greeted them. Penguins sat at the tables, but no one was eating pizza. Next to the cash register, the manager sat with her head in her flippers.

"What's wrong?" a ninja asked.

The penguin sighed. "No one showed up for work today. No servers or chefs! I can't do it all by myself. So there is no pizza tonight."

The ninjas exchanged glances. "Sensei taught us to always be ready for a challenge," Red reminded them. "Looks like we found one! Are we ready to help out?"

The Fire team members answered, "Yes! Let's do it!"

"Oh, thank you!" the manager cried happily. "You'll need these." She took aprons out from under the counter and handed them to the ninjas.

The Fire team sprang into action. First, they took the orders of the hungry customers.

"I'll have a Fish Dish pizza, please," one ordered.

"Make mine a Jelly Bean pizza," another said.

The ninjas dashed around the parlor, taking orders and tossing pizza dough high into the air. Because they were Fire ninjas, they were great at squirting hot sauce on the pizza. Things were going great. But just when the last customer finished, a huge crowd of penguins swarmed inside!

"What's going on?" Red called to the manager over the hungry crowd.

"The play must be over," she explained. "The Stage is right next door, and a huge crowd turned out to see 'Quest for the Golden Puffle'. I guess they all are hungry!"

Red looked thoughtful. "We're good at making spicy pizzas, and we can make them fast," he said. "Mind if I make an announcement."

The manager shrugged. "Do whatever you need to do. I'm glad for the help!"

"Attention, customers! We're having a special on spicy pizzas tonight! Get them while they're hot!" Red called to the crowd.

Red's announcement excited the customers, and the orders for spicy pizzas came rolling in. The Fire ninjas were in their element. They took orders and squirted hot sauce until every customer was happy.

Just when the ninjas thought they would collapse from exhaustion, the manager came over with a big smile on her face. "My servers and chefs just showed up! Thank you so much for all of your help. You can leave now, but whatever can I do to repay you?"

Red smiled. "We need to make one more very special and very spicy pizza!"

While the Fire team ninjas were racing around the Pizza Parlor, the Water team ninjas were searching for a special ingredient. Sensei's favourite drink was tea, and since tea was made with water, they thought it was the perfect water dish to make. But was ordinary tea special enough for Sensei's surprise dinner?

"I heard that one of Sensei's favourite teas is made from the leaves of the rare white O'berry bush," Kit explained. "It grows high in the mountains above the Dojo, but it is very hard to find.

A tea made from those leaves would be very special."

The Water team members agreed this was a good idea and gathered up some hiking and rock-climbing gear. The mountain loomed large above them.

"Here we go!" Kit cried as she threw a grappling hook into the air. It latched onto the mountainside, and the ninjas climbed up one by one.

The ninjas climbed and climbed for what seemed like miles when they passed some wild white puffles playing in the snow.

Kit stopped. "I heard that white puffles are good at finding white O'berry bushes," she whispered. "Let's see if they can help us."

The ninjas slowly walked over to the puffles, using their best stealth moves. But before they could get close, the puffles ran behind some trees and hid.

"Don't be afraid," Kit said gently. "We're just looking for some white O'berry bushes to make a tea for Sensei. Do you know where any are?"

One white puffle slowly peeked out from behind the tree trunk. It looked at the ninjas with its big eyes. Then it slowly hopped out from behind the tree and bounced up and down, as if to say, "yes."

"Awesome!" Kit said. "Can you take us there?"

Again, the cute little white puffle nodded.

"You lead the way," she said. "We'll follow."

The white puffle led the ninjas through a dark forest so thick with trees that there was hardly any sunlight.

"Boo!" one of the ninjas yelled as they walked. Everyone jumped, and the ninjas began to laugh.

"Sorry," he said. "I couldn't resist. It's kind of spooky here."

Luckily, the puffle led them out of the woods and into the bright sunshine. In front of them was a river that was rapidly running down the mountain. The white puffle looked at the river, then back at the ninjas.

"I think it's trying to tell us something," Kit said. She turned to the puffle. "What is it?"

The puffle again looked at the river and then back at Kit.

"Is the white O'berry bush on the other side of the river?" she asked. The white puffle nodded.

"How will we cross it?" she wondered, gazing at the roaring river. She closed her eyes and thought of her ninja training. The best way to overcome water was with frozen snow.

"It's too bad we can't turn this river to ice," she said aloud.

The white puffle began jumping up and down excitedly. The ninjas were confused at first. Then Kit realized something.

"Wait! You can turn things to ice, can't you?" she asked the furry creature.

The white puffle smiled and turned toward the river. It took a deep breath, and then blew out. The frosty air from its mouth froze a small part of the river.

It took another deep breath, and blew out again, freezing another section of the river.

The members of the Water team cheered as the puffle made a bridge of ice so they could cross the river. When it was done, they walked across it single file and found the white O'berry bush.

Kit picked up the white puffle and cuddled it. "Thank you so much! Sensei will be so happy."

As the members of the Water team began to pluck the leaves from the bush, the Snow team were trying to catch a fish for their dish.

"A frozen fish Popsicle is every penguin's favourite treat," Dan reasoned. "And something that chilly is perfect for a snow-themed dish."

His teammates agreed. But in order to make a fish Popsicle, they had to catch a fish!

"Let's head over to the Ski Lodge to do some ice-fishing!" a ninja suggested.

The Snow team ran to the Ski Village and walked over to the Ski Lodge, where penguins can go ice fishing. They picked up some worms and fishing poles before heading out to the ice.

The ninjas seated themselves around holes in the ice. They knew that plenty of fish were swimming underneath the frozen surface. They only needed to catch one to make Sensei's surprise dinner!

Dan frowned. "This could take awhile," he said.

A purple penguin in ninja gear waddled up. His hook was loaded with so many worms they could barely all fit.

"All these worms will get the fish's attention," he suggestion.

"Interesting idea," Dan said. "Let's try it."

Dan lowered his hook into the water and the ninjas quietly waited.

After a few minutes, Dan felt a tug on his line. "I think I got one!" he cried. The tug grew stronger and stronger. He tried to pull up his pole. "That's a big one," he grunted. "I can barely lift it!"

Suddenly, the ice around the hole began to crack. Something was coming out of the water. Something big.

"Look out!" the Dan cried as the head of a huge shark broke through the ice. "It's a shark! Run!"

The shark flopped out onto the ice, snapping its huge mouth at the penguins.

The ninjas quickly backed away from the shark. It flopped on the ice, baring its teeth at them.

"What should we do?" a penguin asked. "We can't just leave it there."

"We're going to have to get it back into the water," Dan said. "If we all push on its tail, we can slide it back into the hole."

The ninjas shuffled their feet nervously. They were all afraid to touch the shark.

"We can do this. We're ninjas!" Dan reminded them. "If we work together, we'll get it done."

The Snow team members agreed. It was time to deal with the shark!

They gathered around the shark's tail, making sure to stay far away from its snapping mouth. "On the count of three, we'll all grab the tail and push," Dan said.

He took a deep breath. "One, two three!"

The ninjas shoved with all of their might. The shark slid across the ice and into the hole, making a huge splash of water as it disappeared.

"Hurray!" the Snow team cheered.

Just then, the splash the shark made came crashing back down again. It soaked all of the ninjas. But it left a fish flopping at their feet!

"I guess that's one way to catch a fish," Dan laughed. "But remind me never to catch a shark again!"

It was time for Sensei's surprise dinner. The Fire team, Water team, and Snow team met at the Dojo.

Sensei sat on a pillow on the floor, smiling at them.

"To thank you for everything you have done for us, Sensei, we have made a special dinner for you," Dan said. "Each dish represents the elements: fire, water and snow."

"Teachers only open the door; you must enter for yourselves," Sensei answered. "I am proud of each and every one of you. Thank you for the dinner. Now let's eat!"

Dan nodded at the teams. Everyone was excited to present

their dish to Sensei.

Red from the Fire team came forward, holding the spicy pizza. Kit from the Water team held a large cup of steaming white O'berry tea. And Dan proudly held the Snow team's fish popsicle on a platter.

The three moved towards Sensei at the same time. Excited, Red started to run–and tripped over his own feet, bumping into Kit! The spicy sauce slid off of the pizza and into the tea.

Startled, Kit dropped her platter. Dan dove to catch it and the fish popsicle slipped from his hands–and landed in the tea. With a plop, the frozen fish landed in the tea.

"Oh no!" Kit whispered. "It's a disaster!"

"What should we do?" Red whispered back. "He's waiting for his special dinner!"

Dan wasn't sure what to do. He knew all of the teams had done their best.

"Sorry, Sensei," he said, handing him the cup of tea. "Things got a little mixed up."

Sensei took the cup and bowed. He held it under his nose and sniffed before pulling out a spoon. All the ninjas watched while he dipped his spoon into the concoction.

Sensei took a sip from the spoon. He closed his eyes. A big smile spread across his face.

"Spicy fish tea soup–my favourite! How did you know?"

The End

# CHATTING WITH CADENCE

Meet Cadence, a penguin who truly grooves to her own beat! She's one of Club Penguin's best dancers. Cadence likes to spend her time in the Night Club, mixing tracks for other penguins to dance to. She's always on the go, but we caught up with her to ask a few questions. Here's what she had to say:

Q: Cadence, you've been called a DJ, musician, dancer and choreographer. Out of all of those, what's your favourite?
Cadence: It's hard to pick! They all go together. Dancing with my puffle Lolz is super cool.

Q: You're known around Club Penguin for your cool sense of style. What is one fashion accessory you can't live without?
Cadence: I wouldn't get far without my shoes! But my headphones rock most of all because they keep the beat close!

Q: With all that dancing, you must work up a thirst! What beverage do you reach for?
Cadence: I wouldn't get very far without loads of water!

Q: Besides the mini-games found at the Night Club: Dance Contest and DJ3K, what Club Penguin games do you like to play?
Cadence: Every game where I can move!

Thanks, Cadence!
Cadence: No problem. And now that we're done—let's go dancing!

# CADENCE'S PLAYLIST

Cadence is getting ready to spin some ice-cold tracks. Help her out by unscrambling the Club Penguin song titles below. Let's get the dance party started!

**1 NINEPUG BDAN OBIEGO**

_ _ _ _ _ _ _   _ _ _ _   _ _ _ _ _ _

**2 ICEP NIW**

_ _ _ _   _ _ _

**3 OG TEWS**

_ _   _ _ _ _

**4 HET ENERICG YAW**

_ _ _   _ _ _ _ _ _ _   _ _ _

**5 ARTSPICK GJI**

_ _ _ _ _ _ _   _ _ _

## SONG BANK

EPIC WIN                PATRICK'S JIG

THE GENERIC WAY         PENGUIN BAND BOOGIE

GO WEST

To hear any of these songs, go to the Night Club and play Dance Contest!

# HOW TO DRAW CADENCE

Follow these simple steps to draw Cadence, Club Penguin's own mix master and dance machine! Use a separte piece of paper, pencil and rubber so you can easily fix any mistakes. Then copy your drawing onto page 51.

## STEP 1

Start drawing Cadence with two simple circles: one for her head and one for her body.

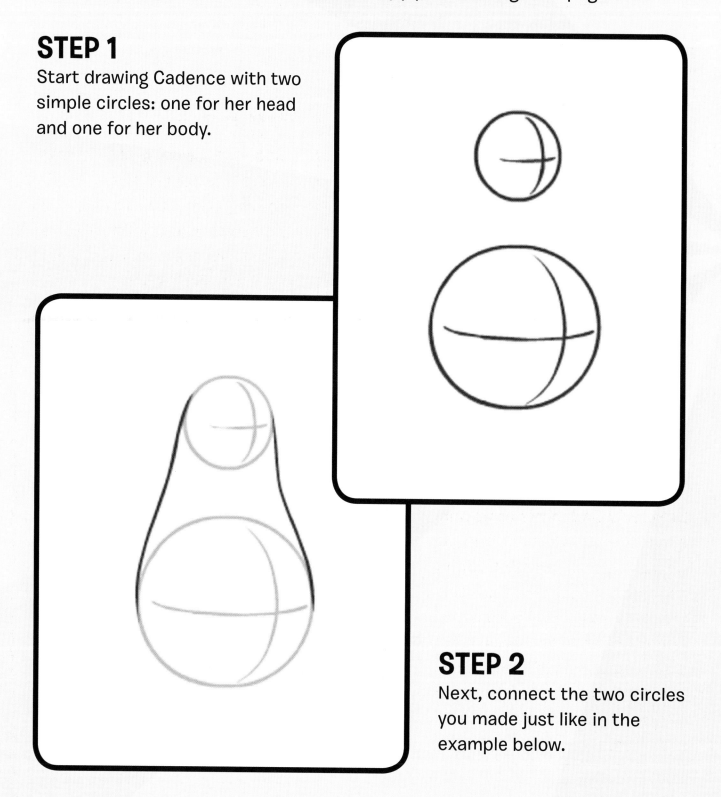

## STEP 2

Next, connect the two circles you made just like in the example below.

## STEP 3

Cadence's smiling face always makes visitors to the Night Club feel welcome. Draw in her eyes and beak, and don't forget her signature eyelashes! No other penguin has them.

## STEP 4

Next, add Cadence's arms and belly line. Now that the body is complete, you can start adding the things that make Cadence look like Cadence. Put dancing shoes on her feet and wavy hair on top of her head. Then add some headphones so Cadence can listen to music wherever she goes.

## STEP 5

Cadence loves to accessorize with a striped scarf and matching wristbands. There are 7 stripes across the top of her scarf, 6 on the left side hanging down, and 3 on the right side. Each wristband has three stripes.

## STEP 6

Cadence is looking good! All that's left is the final step—the detail lines. To make detail lines, draw a dark outline around Cadence's body as shown. Great job! She looks like she's ready to dance hard enough to make the Iceberg tip!

# YOUR DRAWING OF CADENCE

Copy your own drawing of mix master Cadence below!

# STOP THAT INVENTION!

"Over here! Over here!" the pink puffle called out cheerfully.

"You got it!" the blue puffle replied. She sent a red and white ball bouncing across the snow. The pink puffle hopped up to meet it.

"Heads up!" she called out to the black puffle.

The black puffle whizzed past on his skateboard, bopping into the ball at the exact right moment. It soared across the snowy field . . . and then dropped in front of a snoozing orange puffle.

"Z-z-z-z-z-z-z-z." The orange puffle was snoring loudly. The black puffle's skateboard skidded to a stop in front of him.

"Dude, you're drooling all over the ball," he said.

The orange puffle slowly opened his eyes. "What?"

The black puffle sighed. "Who falls asleep during a game of Puffle Ball?"

"Maybe he just needed a nap," the blue puffle said kindly.

The orange puffle yawned, showing off his two large front teeth. "I sure did," he said. "And it felt great!"

Grrrrrrrrrrrrowl . . . The pink puffle looked a little nervous. "What's that noise? Do you think Herbert P. Bear is nearby?"

"That's just my stomach," the orange puffle assured her. "All that napping made me really hungry!"

"I think I saw some O'berry bushes over there," the blue puffle said, looking to the left. "I could go for a snack, too."

"Awesome!" the orange puffle said happily.

He hopped over to the O'berry bushes, and his friends followed him. The o-shaped berries, a favourite food of puffles all over the island, grew on leafy green bushes. There were plenty of low-growing berries, which made it easy for the puffles to gobble them up. But many of the berries grew too high for the puffles to reach.

The orange puffle zipped from one bush to another, chomping on berries as he moved. In a matter of seconds, all of the low-growing berries were gone.

"Wow, that was fast!" the pink puffle remarked.

"I was really hungry," the orange puffle admitted. Then he noticed that he had eaten all of the berries within reach. "Oh no! Look what I did! I'm sorry, guys."

"That's okay," the blue puffle said sweetly. "We can go look for more O'berry bushes somewhere else."

The orange puffle frowned and gazed up at the top of the O'berry bush. "I sure wish we could reach those berries up there," he said.

As soon as he said the words, one of the berries broke away from the bush and started to float through the air. The puffles gasped, and the orange puffle's eyes widened in surprise.

"What do you know? My wish came true!" he cried.

Then a strange whirring sound filled the air, and it was growing louder each second. The puffles turned to see a strange machine rolling across the ground, headed right toward them!

The base of the machine was a small metal box on wheels. A pole was attached to the top of the box, and a basket hung from the middle of the pole. On top of the pole was a yellow arrow, and it was pointing right at the O'berry bush.

The puffles watched in amazement as O-berries floated off of the bush, stuck to the arrow, and then dropped into the basket on the machine. Curious, the orange puffle hopped right up to it.

"What is this thing?" he asked.

"That's my O'berry Attractor," said a brown puffle wearing goggles as he hopped out of the bushes.

"What's an O'berry Attractor?" the blue puffle asked.

"It's a new invention I'm testing out," the brown puffle explained. "You see, I noticed that many puffles had problems reaching O'berries that grow high on the bush. My O'berry Attractor attracts the berries and collects them in this basket."

"Whoa, that's cool," the black puffle said, impressed.

"That's a very useful invention," agreed the blue puffle.

"Mmmmf mmmf mmmf," added the orange puffle, his mouth filled with

O'berries from the basket.

The brown puffle smiled shyly. "Thank you. I'm still testing it, however. I haven't worked out all of the kinks yet."

"It looks fine to me," said the pink puffle.

The brown puffle nodded. "Yes, it does. But sometimes the arrow starts to spin around and around, and the engine moves very fast, and then . . ."

"You mean like that?" the blue puffle asked.

The yellow arrow was spinning wildly on top of the pole, and the engine was starting to shake and rumble loudly.

"Exactly," said the brown puffle. He started fussing with a remote control device. "I just need to adjust the—"

"Dude, watch out!" the black puffle warned.

The machine zoomed forward, nearly slamming into the group of puffles. They all quickly hopped out of the way just in time. The machine chugged away, getting faster and faster as it moved toward the snow.

"It's heading for the Plaza!" the blue puffle cried.

"We have to catch up to it," the brown puffle said worriedly. "I'm not sure what

the O'Berry Attractor is capable of!"

The puffles raced after the runaway machine. Its yellow arrow spun round and round as it picked up speed.

A penguin reading the newspaper looked up, surprised to see the machine whizzing by.

Zap!

The newspaper flew out of her hands, stuck to the arrow, and landed in the basket.

"Hey, my newspaper!" she cried.

"Sorry!" the brown puffle called out, as he and the other puffles hurried by.

"You know that penguins don't understand us, don't you?" the blue puffle asked.

"Of course," the brown puffle replied. "But I'm still sorry!"

The machine kept going. It sped through the forest path and emerged into the crowded Plaza. Penguins milled about on the street. Some were headed to see a play at the Stage. Others were going to the Pet Shop to adopt a puffle. Some were waddling to the Pizza Parlor for a slice of spicy fish pizza and some good conversation.

Two penguins were entering the Pizza Parlor, and the machine whizzed right past them through the open door. A waiter in a red apron was busy scribbling notes on his pad. He thought the machine was a regular customer.

"Would you like a slice of pizza?" the waiter asked.

Zap! A piece of pizza flew out of the flippers of a seated penguin and stuck to the arrow. Then it slid into the basket

and landed on top of the newspaper.

"Hey! My pizza!" the penguin cried.

"Sorry!" the brown puffle called out again. He and the other puffles hopped around the Pizza Parlor, chasing the machine.

"Aw, those puffles are so cute," one penguin remarked.

"Who are you calling cute?" the black puffle grumbled.

The machine sped out the door and back onto the street. The puffles chased after it. They were getting closer, but they had to weave around all of the penguins who were standing around and talking.

The machine's arrow pointed at a penguin wearing sunglasses.

Zap! The sunglasses flew off of the penguin's face, stuck to the arrow, and slid into the basket.

"Hey! My sunglasses!" the startled penguin cried.

"We have to find a way to stop this thing!" the blue puffle called out.

"I know," agreed the brown puffle. "But my controls aren't working. If we could just get ahead of it, perhaps we could slow it down or block its path."

"Everybody get on my skateboard!" the black puffle cried. The puffles quickly jumped on, forming a puffle pyramid on top of the board. The orange puffle teetered on the very top.

"Whoaaaaaa!" he yelled.

Using the skateboard, the puffles zipped past the machine just as the path opened up into the Snow Forts. The black puffle steered the skateboard to the other side of the forts, blocking the path that led to Town.

"It's snowball time!" yelled the black puffle.

The puffles knew just what to do. As the machine rolled toward them, they tossed snowballs at it. The snowballs rained down on the machine, but it caught them, one by one, and dropped them in the basket.

"It's not working!" cried the pink puffle.

"That's 'cause we're using wimpy snowballs," said the black puffle. "We need a really big one to bring down this crazy contraption."

"Let's work together," suggested the blue puffle.

The puffles made a circle and started to push snow into the middle, shaping it into a big snowball. The machine was almost upon them.

"Everybody hop back!" ordered the black puffle.

They bounced out of the way. The yellow arrow pointed at the big snowball. The giant globe of snow slowly, slowly, rose into the air. Then it floated toward the machine.

"Excellent," observed the brown puffle. "The machine seems to be slowing down."

The big snowball slammed into the arrow, then dropped into the basket.

Crash! The machine toppled over sideways and fell into the snow. The engine stopped whirring. The puffles quickly hopped over to it.

"We did it!" cheered the pink puffle.

"Yes, thank you," said the brown puffle, but he sounded very sad. "I'm afraid this invention was a bad idea."

"That's not true," said the pink puffle. "It's a great idea. You just need to fix it."

The brown puffle shook his head. "It's too risky. I must face the facts. I've failed."

"Don't give up, dude," urged the black puffle.

But the brown puffle just sighed.

"Hey, do you want to play Puffle Ball with us?" asked the blue puffle.

"No thank you," said the brown puffle. "I'm not in the mood."

The puffles felt bad about leaving their new friend, but there didn't seem to be a way to change his mind.

"If you change your mind, come find us," the blue puffle said, but the brown puffle didn't answer.

The puffles went back to their play spot in the snow. They formed a big circle and started to play Puffle Ball again. The blue puffle bounced the ball to the pink puffle. The pink puffle bounced the ball to the black puffle. The black puffle bounced the ball to the orange puffle . . . who wasn't there!

"Dude, are you taking a nap again?" the black puffle asked.

"I'm over here!" the orange puffle called from within the trees. "Come quickly!"

The puffles followed the sound of their friend's voice. They found the orange puffle at the bottom of a very tall tree.

"Up there!" the orange puffle said, looking up.

High, high in the branches was a little purple puffle. He looked very frightened.

"What are you doing up there?" the blue puffle called up.

"I was walking along, looking for O'berries, when a strong wind whipped up," answered the purple puffle. "It carried me high up in the air! I managed to hop onto this tree branch, but now I can't get down."

"Don't worry! We'll help you!" the blue puffle assured him.

"How are we going to get way up there?" the orange puffle asked.

"I could try my trampoline," the pink puffle suggested. She set up her trampoline under the tree and then bounced on it. She bounced higher . . . and higher . . . and higher . . . but she still couldn't reach the purple puffle.

"What now?" the blue puffle wondered.

"I wish we had a machine that could get him down from there," said the orange puffle.

The black puffle hopped over to him. "Dude, you're a genius. There is a machine that can help. The brown puffle's machine."

"But it's broken," the blue puffle pointed out.

"I'm sure he can fix it," the pink puffle said hopefully. "He's very smart."

"The black puffle and I will go find him," said the blue puffle. "You two stay here and watch the white puffle."

"Got it!" the orange puffle and pink puffle replied.

The blue puffle and black puffle hurried back to the Snow Forts. They found the brown puffle on the path, pushing the machine in front of him.

"I'm so glad we found you," said the blue puffle. "We need your machine. It's an emergency!"

"But this machine is a failure," the brown puffle protested.

"It's an awesome machine," said the black puffle. "You just need to fix it."

"There's no time to talk," said the blue puffle impatiently. "A purple puffle is stuck in a tree. We've got to help him!"

She hopped next to the brown puffle and started to push. The black puffle joined in. The three puffles pushed the machine all the way to the tree.

"Hooray!" said the pink puffle. "I knew you would come."

The brown puffle looked up into the tree. "This appears to be a very serious situation," he said. He didn't look sad anymore. He looked determined. "All right! I'll fix it."

The brown penguin quickly got to

work. His eyes gleamed behind his red-rimmed goggles as he used his tools to tinker with the machine. The other puffles watched quietly as he pressed buttons and crossed wires. Finally, he hopped back from the machine.

"I think I've got it," he said proudly. "But first, a test."

The brown puffle used the remote to aim the arrow at a pine cone on the tree. Then he pressed a button, and the pine cone gently floated off the tree and dropped into the basket.

"Perfect!" cheered the pink puffle.

"It does seem to be working smoothly," the brown puffle agreed. "All right. Let's give this a try."

The arrow spun around and pointed up at the white puffle in the tree.

"Stay calm!" the brown puffle called up to him. "I'll make sure you go very slowly."

"Okay," the purple puffle said nervously.

The brown puffle pressed a button, and the white puffle floated off of the tree branch. He slowly, slowly dropped through the air and landed safely in the basket.

"Hooray!" the puffles cheered.

The orange puffle was amazed. "Whoa. That was like magic!" he said.

"Actually, it's science," the brown puffle corrected him.

The purple puffle hopped out of the basket. "I don't care how you did it, I'm just glad you did," he said. "Thank you so much."

The brown puffle smiled. "I guess my

O'berry Attractor works."

"It's also a Puffle Rescuer," the pink puffle pointed out.

"And a Pizza Grabber," added the orange puffle.

"Let's celebrate. Who wants to play Puffle Ball?" asked the blue puffle.

"I do!" each of the puffles yelled.

The puffles got in a big circle. The blue puffle bounced the ball to the pink puffle. The pink puffle bounced the ball to the purple puffle. The purple puffle bounced it to the brown puffle, who caught it with his machine. The machine bounced it to the black puffle, who caught it as he whizzed by on his skateboard. And the black puffle bounced it to the orange puffle . . . who was fast asleep and drooling in the snow.

The black puffle shook his head. He turned to the brown puffle.

"Do you think you can invent a Drool Attractor next?" he asked.

The brown puffle smiled. "Why not? Right now, I feel like I could invent anything!

The End

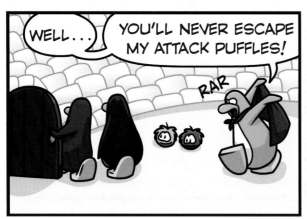

HEY! WHAT'RE YOU UP TO?

OH, JUST TAKING MY PUFFLE FOR A WALK.

HEY! WHATCHA UP TO?

EH. JUST TAKING MY PENGUIN FOR A WALK. YOU KNOW HOW THEY CAN GET.

# ANSWER KEY

**PAGE 8**
## WORD TREASURE HUNT

Here are some words we found.
You may have found more!

Rockhopper: chop, chopper, choke, chore, coop, cop, cope, copper, core, hoop, hop, hope, peck, perch, pock, poke, poker, poor, rock, rope

Migrator: gator, goat, grim, oar, oat, rag, rat, rig, roar, tag, tar

Treasure: art, arts, as, at, ear, ears, eat, eats, rare, rats, rats, rear, ruse, rut, sea, sear, seat, see, seer, star, stare, steer, sure, tar, tea, teas, tee, tees, tear, tears.

**PAGE 10**
## MIGRATOR MAZE

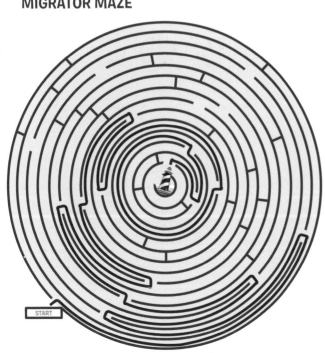

START

**PAGE 11**
## TELSECOPE TEST

**PAGE 13**
## A MEETING MIX-UP

|  | PET SHOP | ICEBERG | GIFT SHOP | STADIUM |
|---|---|---|---|---|
| BLACK PENGUIN | BLACK PENGUIN | BLACK PENGUIN |  |  |
| PINK PENGUIN |  |  | PINK PENGUIN |  |
| LIME GREEN PENGUIN | LIME GREEN PENGUIN | LIME GREEN PENGUIN |  |  |
| PURPLE PENGUIN |  |  |  | PURPLE PENGUIN |

**PAGE 16**
## FIND THE MISSING COLOUMNS

| G | T | Z | F | E | N | O | Z | K | C | U | B | A | G | U | Y |
|---|---|---|---|---|---|---|---|---|---|---|---|---|---|---|---|
| B | J | Y | G | L | Z | B | Q | K | I | P | N | Z | E | F | D |
| N | C | O | I | F | T | Q | U | O | T | C | E | G | T | Y | N |
| L | S | Z | H | Y | D | F | Y | F | C | O | X | N | P | G | E |
| T | R | U | C | R | Q | J | F | R | M | T | G | U | V | G | W |
| T | J | H | Q | O | H | O | D | J | A | I | H | I | B | G | S |
| I | S | R | C | T | R | K | Y | W | T | N | I | E | L | A | F |
| S | Z | T | E | S | P | E | S | T | N | G | D | L | I | R | L |
| E | T | S | E | E | B | S | A | W | U | E | D | I | S | V | A |
| E | I | B | H | R | U | E | B | V | A | V | E | E | H | P | S |
| V | L | D | L | U | C | L | F | X | K | E | N | O | E | J | H |
| H | M | R | O | T | W | E | V | M | S | N | P | I | D | U | G |
| J | Y | G | S | A | Z | F | S | F | A | T | I | P | L | E | P |
| M | U | E | V | E | B | H | O | W | B | S | N | G | L | G | A |
| H | Q | N | F | F | R | G | U | S | R | I | D | D | L | E | S |
| K | C | D | X | Z | C | C | F | C | K | T | W | Z | V | A | N |

# ANSWER KEY

**PAGE 17**
**PUFFLE PROBLEM**

1. New Puffle Discovered
2. Rockhopper Interview
3. Puffle Party is Here
4. Water Dojo Tour with Sensei
5. Penguin Costume Contest
6. Are Elite Agents Among Us?
7. In Style with Cadence
8. Gary's Gadget Review
9. Tips for Mini-Games
10. Mystery Ship Spotted at Beach

**PAGE 29**
**GARY'S MEMORY TEST**

1. 4
2. 3
3. Headphones
4. Green, purple, blue, and yellow
5. Feeding the puffles
6. O'berry
7. Puffles
8. Yellow
9. O-berries
10. Purple

**PAGE 31**
**EPF CROSSWORD PUZZLE**

|   | ¹S |   | ²H | O | L | O | ³G | R | A | M | R | O | O | M |
|---|---|---|---|---|---|---|---|---|---|---|---|---|---|---|
|   | P |   |   |   |   |   | A |   |   |   |   |   |   |   |
|   | Y |   |   |   |   |   | R |   |   |   |   |   |   |   |
|   | P |   |   |   |   |   | Y |   |   |   | ⁴T |   |   |   |
|   | ⁵H | E | R | B | E | R | T |   | ⁶F | I | E | L | D | O | P |
|   | O |   |   |   |   |   | H |   |   |   | L |   |   |   |
|   | N |   |   |   | ⁷T | H | E | D | I | R | E | C | T | O | R |
|   | E |   |   |   |   |   | G |   |   |   | P |   |   |   |
|   |   |   | ⁸C | O | M | M | A | N | D | R | O | O | M |   |
|   |   |   |   |   |   |   | D |   |   |   | R |   |   |   |
|   | ⁹A | G | E | N | T | G |   |   |   | T |   |   |   |
|   |   |   |   |   |   | E |   |   |   |   |   |   |   |
|   |   |   |   |   |   | T |   |   |   |   |   |   |   |
| ¹⁰E | L | I | T | E | G | E | A | R |   |   |   |   |   |
|   |   |   |   |   |   | U |   |   |   |   |   |   |   |
|   |   |   |   |   |   | Y |   |   |   |   |   |   |   |

**PAGE 35**
**PUFFLE PATTERNS**

1
2
3
4
5

# ANSWER KEY

## PAGE 36
### SENSEI'S SEARCH

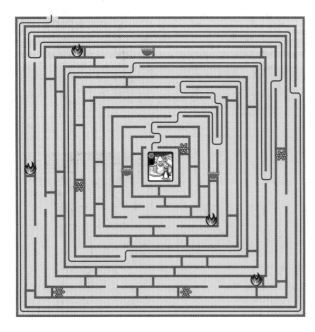

## PAGE 47
### CADENCE'S PLAYLIST

1. Penguin Band Boogie
2. Epic Win
3. Go West
4. The Generic Way
5. Patrick's Jig

## PAGE 37
### SPOT THE DIFFERENCES